Relax with
Romantic Piano

35 Beautiful Pieces

Selected by
Samantha Ward

ED 13851
ISMN 979-0-2201-3683-2
ISBN 978-1-84761-399-8

www.schott-music.com

Mainz · London · Berlin · Madrid · New York · Paris · Prague · Tokyo · Toronto
© 2016 SCHOTT MUSIC Ltd, London · Printed in Germany

ED 13851
British Library Cataloguing-in-Publication Data.
A catalogue record for this book is available from the British Library
ISMN 979-0-2201-3683-2
ISBN 978-1-84761-399-8
© 2016 Schott Music Ltd, London

Cover design by www.josellopis.com
French translation: Michaëla Rubi
German translation: Heike Brühl
Printed in Germany S&Co.9286

Contents

Introduction

Schott Music's *Relax With* series is designed to help you unwind with some of the piano repertoire's greatest works, alongside lesser known pieces from the Baroque period right through to the 20th century. I have tried to include as many different styles and techniques as possible, whilst remaining within the boundaries of 'relaxing' pieces of music. It has been particularly enjoyable for me to delve into new works in producing these five collections, and to be able to include pieces by the most famous composers as well as by those who are less well known, such as Johanna Senfter, Xaver Scharwenka and, in the Folk collection, works from around the world by Georges Ivanovitch Gurdjieff and Thomas de Hartmann. I hope you enjoy the collections and that you too get to know new pieces along the way.

In this Romantic collection, there are transcriptions of pieces which were not originally written for piano, as well as some of my personal favourites from my own repertoire such as Brahms' Intermezzo Op. 118 No. 2 and Chopin's 'Raindrop' Prelude Op. 28.

Samantha Ward

Samantha Ward is a British Concert pianist, and founder and Artistic Director of the international festival and summer school, *Piano Week*. For more information, please visit **www.samanthaward.org**

Introduction

La collection « Moments détente » des éditions Schott est conçue pour vous aider à vous relaxer grâce à quelques-unes des plus grandes œuvres du répertoire pour piano ainsi que d'autres moins connues, de la période baroque à nos jours. Je me suis attaché à inclure dans cette sélection des techniques et des styles aussi variés que possible sans perdre de vue les propriétés « relaxantes » de la musique. J'ai eu beaucoup de plaisir à rechercher de nouveaux morceaux dans la perspective des cinq recueils de cette collection et me suis réjoui d'avoir la possibilité de choisir aussi bien des œuvres des compositeurs les plus célèbres que celles d'autres bien moins connus tels que Johanna Senfter ou Xaver Scharwenka ou, parmi les musiques du monde, celles de Georges Ivanovitch Gurdjieff et Thomas de Hartmann. J'espère que vous apprécierez ces recueils et qu'ils vous permettront à vous aussi de découvrir de nouvelles œuvres.

Vous trouverez dans ce recueil consacré à la musique romantique des transcriptions de pièces écrites initialement pour d'autres instruments que le piano ainsi que quelques-uns de mes morceaux de prédilection tels que l'*Intermezzo* Op. 118 n° 2 de Brahms et le prélude dit « de la goutte d'eau » Op. 28 de Chopin.

Samantha Ward

Fondatrice et directrice artistique du festival international et des cours d'été « Piano Week », Samantha Ward est une pianiste concertiste britannique. Vous trouverez davantage d'informations sur son site **www.samanthaward.org**

Einleitung

Mit der Reihe *Relax With* von Schott Music kann man mit vielen bekannten Klavierwerken sowie einigen weniger bekannten Stücken vom Barock bis zum 20. Jahrhundert entspannen. Ich habe versucht, so viele verschiedene Stilrichtungen und Techniken wie möglich zu berücksichtigen und dabei trotzdem den Aspekt der Entspannung nicht aus den Augen zu verlieren. Bei der Zusammenstellung der fünf Sammlungen war es für mich besonders schön, neue Werke kennen zu lernen und Stücke der ganz großen, aber auch Stücke von weniger bekannten Komponisten wie z. B. Johanna Senfter, Xaver Scharwenka und – in der Volksmusik-Sammlung – Werke aus aller Welt von Georges Ivanovitch Gurdjieff und Thomas de Hartmann in die Bände aufzunehmen. Ich wünsche Ihnen viel Spaß mit den Sammlungen und hoffe, dass auch Sie darin einige neue Stücke finden.

Diese Sammlung mit romantischen Stücken enthält Bearbeitungen von Werken, die ursprünglich nicht für Klavier geschrieben waren, sowie einige meiner persönlichen Lieblingsstücke aus meinem Repertoire, z. B. Brahms Intermezzo Op. 118 Nr. 2 und Chopins „Regentropfen-Prélude" Op. 28.

Samantha Ward

Samantha Ward ist eine britische Konzertpianistin sowie die Gründerin und künstlerische Leiterin von *Piano Week*, einem internationalen Festival und Ferienkurs. Weitere Informationen finden Sie im Internet unter **www.samanthaward.org**

Sad at Heart

Banges Herzelein

Robert Fuchs
(1847–1927)

From the Schott edition *Romantic Piano Anthology 1* (ED 12912)

Dedication

A mi hijo Eduardo*

Enrique Granados
(1867–1916)

* To my son Eduardo / À mon fils Eduardo / Für mein Sohn Eduardo

From the Schott edition *Romantic Piano Anthology 2* (ED 12913)

Album Leaf

Antonín Dvořák
(1841–1904)

Moderato [♩ = 112–116]

*vroucně**

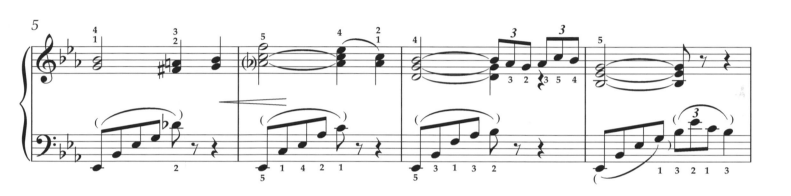

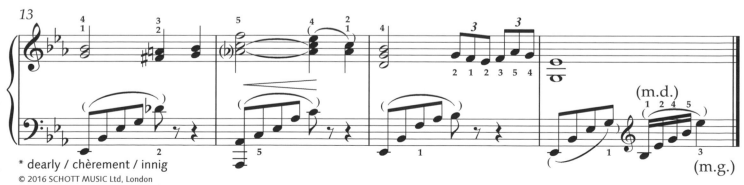

(m.d.)

(m.g.)

* dearly / chèrement / innig

© 2016 SCHOTT MUSIC Ltd, London

From the Schott edition *Romantic Piano Anthology 2* (ED 12913)

A Little Study
Op. 68, No. 14

Robert Schumann
(1810–1856)

Leise und sehr egal zu spielen

From the Schott edition *Album for the Young* (ED 9010)

*) The small notes are part of the original text (autograph and first edition).
 Die kleinen Noten stehen im Autograph und Erstdruck, sind also ad libitum-Zusätze von Schumann.

Prelude
E minor
Op. 28/4

Frédéric Chopin
(1810–1849)

Largo ♩ = 72

From the Schott edition *Best of Piano Classics* (ED 9060)

Lullaby
from *Studies* Op. 109

Friedrich Burgmüller
(1806–1874)

From the Schott edition *Night and Dreams* (ED 9048)

Waltz
Op. 39/15

Johannes Brahms
(1833–1897)

From the Schott edition *Romantic Piano Anthology 3* (ED 12914)

Sweet Dreams
from *Children's Album*
Op. 39/21

Pyotr Ilyich Tchaikovsky
(1840–1893)

From the Schott edition *Piano Classics* (ED 9036)

Lullaby
F major
Op. 49/4

Johannes Brahms
(1833–1897)

From the Schott edition *Lullaby in F major* (ED0 7635)

Prelude
Op. 28/6

Frédéric Chopin
(1810–1849)

From the Schott edition *The Classical Piano Method: Repertoire Collection 3* (ED 13573)

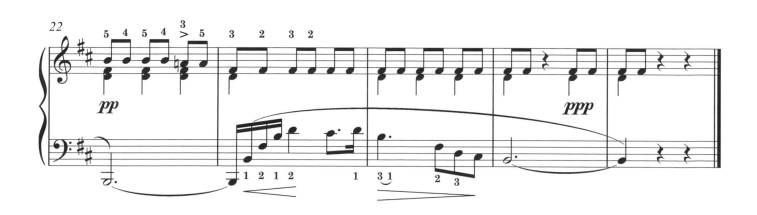

Arietta

from *Lyric Pieces*, Op. 12/1

Edvard Grieg
(1843–1907)

Poco Andante e sostenuto ♩ = 84

From the Schott edition *Pianissimo: Für Elise* (ED 20044)

From Foreign Lands and People

from *Scenes from Childhood*

Op. 15/1

Robert Schumann
(1810–1856)

From the Schott edition *Pianissimo: Für Elise* (ED 20044)

Mazurka
G minor
Op. 67/2

Frédéric Chopin
(1810–1849)

From the Schott edition *Easy Romantic Piano Music: Band 2* (ED 8277)

Tango

Isaac Albéniz
(1860–1909)

From the Schott edition *Tango Meets Jazz* (ED 20878)

To a Wild Rose
Op. 51/1

Edward MacDowell
(1860–1908)

From the Schott edition *Romantic Piano Anthology 3* (ED 12914)

In the Evening
Op. 88/2

Heinrich Hofmann
(1842–1902)

From the Schott edition *Easy Romantic Piano Music: Band 1* (ED 4748)

Il vecchio castello

Modest Mussorgsky
(1839–1881)

From the Schott edition *Pictures at an Exhibition* (ED 525)

Dance Arabe

Pyotr Ilyich Tchaikovsky
(1840–1893)

From the Schott edition *Nutcracker Suite* (ED 2394)

Songs Without Words
Op. 30/3

Felix Mendelssohn-Bartholdy
(1809–1847)

Adagio non troppo

From the Schott edition *Songs Without Words* (ED 9012)

Ernste Gedanken

Johanna Senfter
(1879–1961)

Adagio ma non troppo

From the Schott edition *Johanna Senfter: Selected Works* (ED 8275)

Evening Song

from *Album for the Young*

Op. 17/11

Max Reger
(1873–1916)

*) The thump coupled with the syncopated pedal takes the lead of the melodie line. /
Der Daumen führt die Melodielinie, untersützt durch synkopiertes Pedal.

From the Schott edition *Easy Romantic Piano Music: Band 2* (ED 8277)

Prelude
Op. 11/5

Alexander Scriabin
(1872–1915)

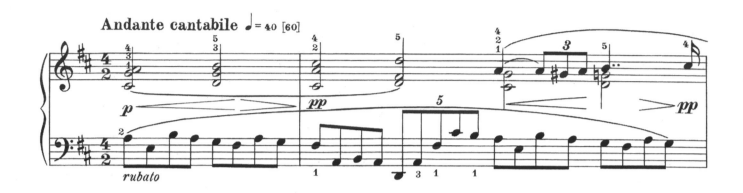

From the Schott edition *Scriabin: Selected Works* (ED 7523)

A Teardrop
Op. posth. No. 18

Modest Mussorgsky
(1839–1881)

From the Schott edition *Piano Classics* (ED 9036)

Chanson
Op. 2/2

Bedřich Smetana
(1824–1884)

From the Schott edition *Smetana: Selected Works* (ED 7079)

Barcarolle
Op. 62/4

Xaver Scharwenka
(1850–1924)

From the Schott edition *Romantic Piano Anthology 3* (ED 12914)

Waltz
Op. 69/1 (posth.)

Frédéric Chopin
(1810–1849)

From the Schott edition *Chopin: Selected Piano Works – Vol.2* (ED 504)

Raindrop Prélude
Op. 28/15

Frédéric Chopin
(1810–1849)

From the Schott edition *Piano Classics* (ED 9036)

*) small hands: leave out notes in brackets / bei kleinen Händen: eingeklammerte Noten weglassen

Waltz
Op. 34/2

Frédéric Chopin
(1810–1849)

From the Schott edition *Chopin: Selected Piano Works – Vol.1* (ED 503)

Kleine Klavierstücke
S192, No. 2

Franz Liszt
(1811–1886)

From the Schott edition *Liszt: Album Leaves and Short Piano Pieces* (ED 9054)

Intermezzo
Slumber Song, E♭ major
Op. 117/1

Johannes Brahms
(1833–1897)

Andante moderato

Un poco più andante

This page is left blank to save an unnecessary page turn.

Song Without Words
Op. 19/1

Felix Mendelssohn Bartholdy
(1809–1847)

From the Schott edition *Songs Without Words* (ED 9012)

Consolations
No. 3

Franz Liszt
(1811–1886)

*) The sustained bassnote should be silently depressed when damping the strings; it should, however, be struck afresh if occasion demands. /
La longue note à la basse est à appuyer, sans faire résonner, à chaque changement de pédal; toutefois, la faire entendre, si le besoin sen faisait sentir. /
Die lang gehaltene Bassnote je beim Wechsel des Pedals stumm niederdrücken, bei Bedarf aber neu anschlagen!

From the Schott edition *Liszt: Selected Works* (ED 507)

This page is left blank to save an unnecessary page turn.

Morning Mood

Op. 46/1

Edvard Grieg
(1843–1907)

From the Schott edition *Grieg: Selected Works* (ED 505)

Intermezzo
Op. 118, No. 2

Johannes Brahms
(1833–1897)

From the Schott edition *Six pieces for Piano* (ED 1647)

Autumn Song

October, No. 10 from *The Seasons*
Op. 37/2

Pyotr Ilyich Tchaikovsky
(1840–1893)

Andante doloroso e molto cantabile

From the Schott edition *Tchaikovsky: Selected Works* (ED 516)